Shades of Eden™

Creating the New Dream

Mandala Coloring Journal

Belongs to.............................

Beginning..............................

This Mandala Coloring Journal provides support for spiritual growth and wellbeing. It does not replace medical or psychological diagnosis, counseling and treatment.

Introduction

"The Mandala... signifies the wholeness of self." Carl Jung

You have within your hands, a unique gift, the opportunity to create your own personal spiritual journey of awakening!

Shades of Eden™ is a journal with a difference—it contains inspirational messages, high vibrational art, mandala templates to color and contemplate, and plenty of pages for your own journaling and creative inspiration. Its purpose is to support and encourage you to activate more of your own inner Divine Self and express this within your daily life.

Coloring the mandalas offers tremendous potential for interaction with the frequencies and vibrations of creation, which helps you to remember your True and Authentic Self.

Journaling the experience helps take you even deeper, and creates a beautiful record of the unfolding adventure.

Through the "Shades of Eden" you will be experiencing energies that are the frequencies and vibrations of the New Earth. Feel the energy of Universal Love as it surrounds, warms and supports you!

Enter, and create your own unique journey...

With Love and Blessings,

Barbara Evans

Guidelines

Inspirational Messages and Images

Inspirational messages of Healing, Awakening and Transformation are interwoven between the coloring mandalas and journal pages. These messages are for you to contemplate, and spend some time with. The images are carefully selected to provide energetic support; they hold inspirational messages in visual form. Focus on connecting with the intentions of each message and the beautiful vibrations of the images themselves... you may even wish to place your left hand upon the page and let it rest there, absorbing the essence of the message as you do so.

Mandala Coloring Templates

The 11 mandala templates are founded on Sacred Geometry. Sacred Geometry is the Language of the Universe, and the designs carry a healing power within them. One definition of Healing is remembering our WHOLENESS... our Body, Mind and Spirit. By choosing to actively interact with the symbols of creation, you are inviting new levels of your True Self to awaken. It is a process that takes place beyond the logic of thought. As you color the patterns you are being invited to connect with deeper aspects within yourself... this will happen easily and naturally if you simply hold the intention for it to be so.

The more deeply you allow yourself to be involved, the greater the potential benefit

Journal Pages

Each mandala coloring template is accompanied by journal pages... use them to record your experience of this journey into the vibrations and frequencies of the *Shades of Eden*™ for they are the frequencies and vibrations of the New Earth. Be aware of thoughts, feelings and dreams that pass through your heart and mind, as you focus on this creative spiritual journey.

Blank Pages

The blank pages, watermarked with the geometry of Divinity, provide the option for you to create your own images, or whatever feels right to you ... they may also be left as they are!

Balance and Harmony

Balance within our life is an important aspect in the creation of Harmony.... Harmony within us, and Harmony around us, contributes to our experience of JOY and INNER PEACE and is a vital component of the New Earth. Each mandala template Interweaves Balance and Harmony within its design.

Personalized Healing Journey

By creating your own journey, you will discover new insights about your true and authentic self. Embrace and enjoy this profound experience, as it offers a unique way to explore and define your spiritual growth and evolution.

Healing

I Allow the Vibrations of LOVE
to Open and Heal my Heart

Flower of Life in Feminine Form

FEELING WITH THE HEART. As you color this mandala, remember a special place in nature that you love… feel the beauty of this place with every color that you choose.

Feel yourself connecting through your heart to the Earth, and know you are also connecting via Sacred Geometry to the Language of the Universe. See these connections blossoming within your life.

Flower of Life in Masculine Form

THOUGHT AND THE MIND. As you color the Flower of Life a second time, notice the pattern has rotated through 90 degrees. Through this mandala, you are invited to connect with the Wisdom of the Universe. Hold the intention of connecting with Wisdom. Experience the scientific, mathematical and logical side of your being grow stronger, supporting your ability to put ideas into action.

The energy of Love speaks to my
Heart and connects to my Soul...
Encouraging a new journey to
begin...

Love surrounds ME, Love is within
ME, Love Heals ME...
I am the embodiment of LOVE

Genesis in Feminine Form

CREATIVITY. The six central petals are "Lotus Petals"; they hold a "V" formation signifying Feminine Energy. You are invited to explore more deeply your feminine gifts of creativity, grace and intuition. Reclaiming, honoring and encouraging these feminine aspects of ourselves is an important step in realizing our wholeness. Which colors are calling as you set yourself free in this experience?

Genesis in Masculine Form

LOGIC. *The Masculine Genesis Pattern is rotated through 90 degrees compared to the Feminine form. The two central "Lotus Petals" form a vertical line. You are invited to connect with the masculine side of your being which brings order, structure and clarity... important gifts for manifestation. Which colors do you choose in order to strengthen these masculine gifts that help manifest your dreams?*

Awakening

I Choose to Awaken,
Connect to, and Embody
my Wholeness and Divinity

The Unity Symbol

BALANCE AND HARMONY: The Unity Symbol brings together the Feminine and Masculine Genesis Patterns, embodying perfect balance. It's energy brings integrates creativity and intuition with the ability to manifest through order and action.

As you color this mandala, focus on making deep connections with all aspects of your self. Which colors inspire Unity, Harmony and Wholeness?

Frequencies of Wholeness and
Rejuvenation surround me..

Encouraging me to
remember my perfection

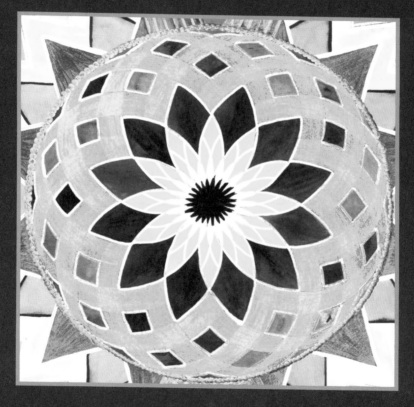

I Rejoice in the Beauty that I AM

Love Symbol

LOVE. The Love Symbol mandala has ten "Lotus Petals" at its heart. The petals are created by ten outer circles meeting within the central circle.

The frequencies offer a powerful connection to "Venus" ... known as the Planet and Goddess of Love.

Call upon the energy of Love to activate within you; notice how you feel. Which colors are calling to you?

Divine Love Symbol

DIVINE LOVE. This 10 : 10 mandala represents the frequencies and vibrations of Unconditional Divine Love, the energy of the Universe and true energy behind all of creation. Allow yourself to connect with these fundamental vibrations; imagine breathing in Divine Love as you are guided to the colors that encourage beauty and joy to blossom within your life.

Transformation

I Choose to walk a pathway of
expansion into Peace, Beauty,
Joy and Unconditional Love

Unity Consciousness

ONENESS. Eleven "Lotus Petals" are at the heart of this mandala. Eleven is a powerful master number and brings special energies into the template. The energy speaks of our connection to all that exists; it speaks of Oneness. Coloring this mandala helps you remember these connections on a very deep and personal level.

As you color, know you are One with the Universe.

Gateway to Higher Consciousness

HIGHER CONSCIOUSNESS: This 11 : 11 mandala presents a gateway to Higher Consciousness, taking us to a place of Oneness on many levels, and infusing our life with inner peace, and joy. Higher Consciousness is the gateway to the New Earth , the frequencies and vibrations of Eden. Allow your inner self to guide color choices, as you explore these beneficial vibrations of Potential.

Surrounded by energies of shift and change...

Opportunities for personal growth and transformation abound

I AM Peace, Beauty, Joy and Unconditional Love

Awakening Our Divinity

AWAKENING DIVINITY. We are all vast and magnificent Beings, children of the Divine Creator. We hold within us a Divine Blueprint that codes for our Full and True Potential. Coloring this mandala helps us transform through awakening more of this Blueprint. Hold the intention of Awakening your Divinity, as you interweave your intuitively chosen colors.

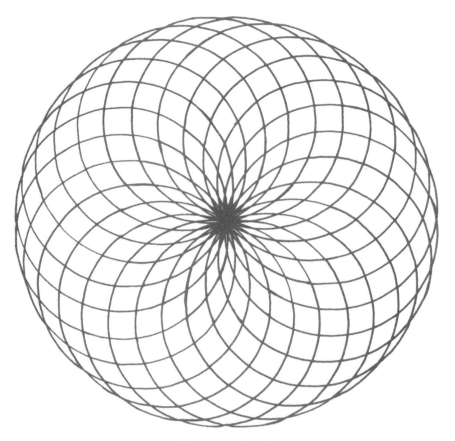

Divine Unity

POSSIBILITIES. This mandala of Divine Unity helps you connect to new possibilities… there are no limitations. As you color, bring forth the feelings deep within your heart that yearn to be expressed, and the inspiring thoughts within your mind that call to be heard.

This final Mandala in Shades of Eden is a portal to the expression of your Highest Self.

Barbara Evans is an author and transformational healing artist whose award-winning book, *Messages of Universal Wisdom* and beautiful *Image Key* paintings have gained international recognition. The *Image Keys* radiate vibrations which contribute to healing via the raising of consciousness, and deepening the connection with our True Self. Barbara's artwork is now the foundation of a new energy healing modality, The Eden Method... The Art of Raising Frequency⁻.

Barbara's vision is to help Create a New Earth and New Dream, based on Unconditional Love, Peace and Joy.

Learn more about Barbara and her work at:
CrystalWingsHealingArt.com